THE FIFTH MAD REPORT ON

SPY vs SPY

by Antonio Prohias
Edited by Albert B. Feldstein

WARNER BOOKS

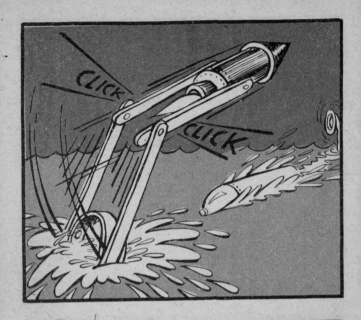

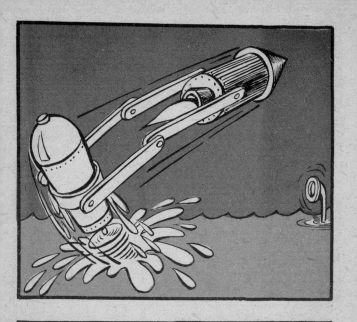

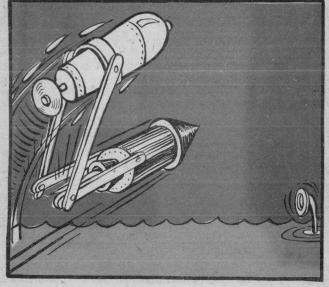

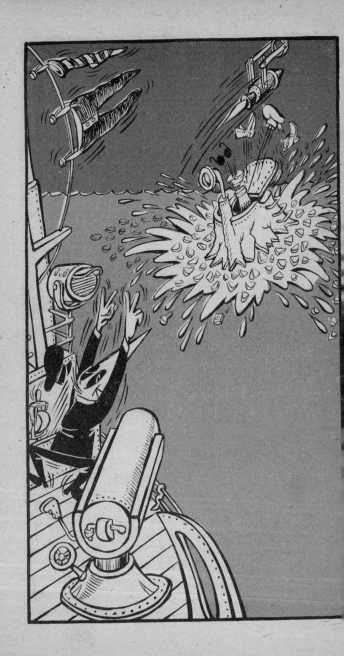

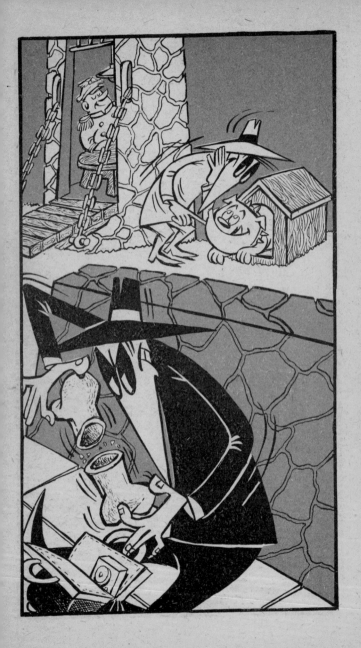

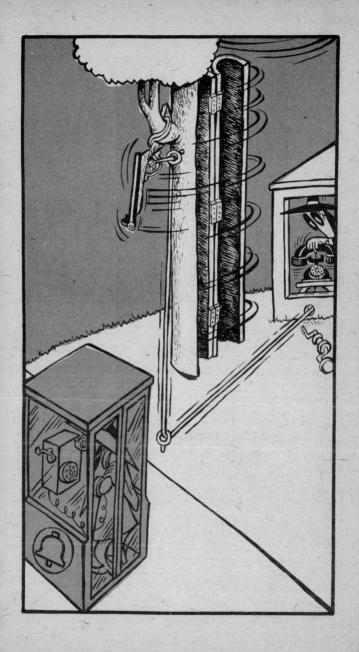

CLICK

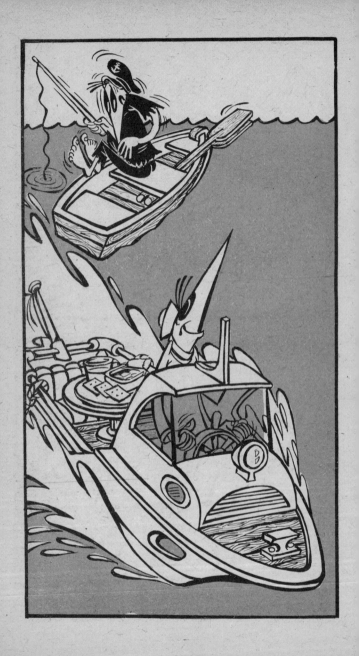

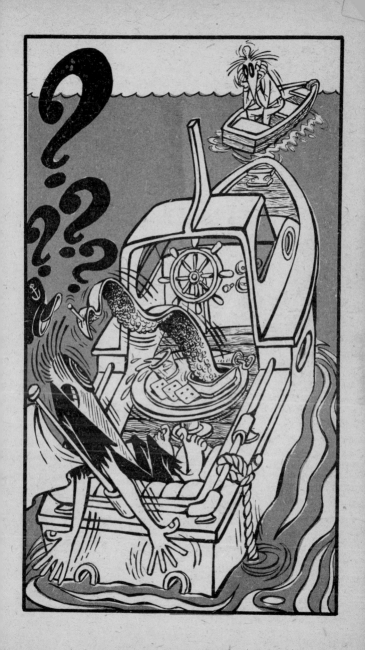

MINI
MAGNETIC
MINE

THE NEW SPY

SUPER BLACK MISSILES!!!

...lways said, if you're
n't coddle them.

it is my belief that
tand the English lang
here's no necessity fo
g, the next thing the
om there it is ju
estioning an *orde*
rule of the sea that
ould have one hand f
r. I subscribe to that.
st their right hand for
ft hand for holding
ing with their other h
llow in a storm tryin
and. I was about to l
d if it didn't turn ou
y amusing incident.
nusement brings up t
n on board a ship is
here are, let's face it
the cockpit or in th
u frankly, they are
owadays when—I m
nen aren't what th
't what they used
y are told and do
I've met preciou
time who have e
of beating to w
e direction,
nt to

Monster by SORC competi
Dr. Jekyll and took off t
At first seas were calm as
stopping occasionally for
d—yet we still carried the
s had been made for boom
g passages. *Finisterre* was s
vo-man watches always felt
ertaken by a depression wh
me down all the way to a #
nges. And, although happ
the Azores to prove how
e, between Fayal and Sa
mmense seas from a Forc
th without missing sleep
tar across the Portuguese
ghride, but it was with su
eport we had sailed alm
—only 635 of them ra
per day, perhaps somett
erline boat with wine bott
wing table at lunch a
nenu called for a white. I
liment *Finisterre* ever t
t came the morning follo
ter nearly at sec
Straits errac
reakfast
ay for a sail!"
t down to the qu
ing to Africa.
terre got home after
h and Italian coasts,
stern-to in front of
ule makers had bee
e it or not, welcom
l take. Even no
k the maximum
horus of woe—b
h came down
t made eligi
t of installi
years lat
came
p. Th
ctl

bility of six bunks, including tw
reasonably sized galley and a
e. The enclosed heads ar
d of the mast and ami
d it the bunks could
e well upholstered
nyl material. She
the woodwork
air of stabil
cots in
satisfact
shb

MOTHS

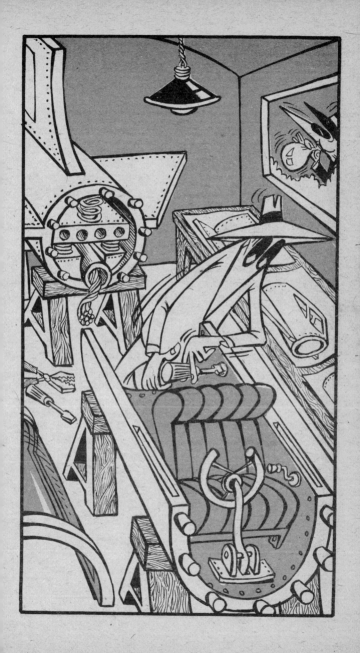

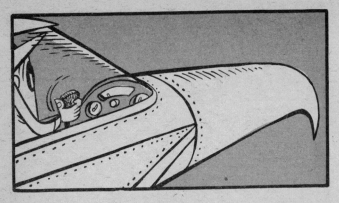

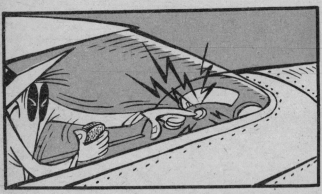

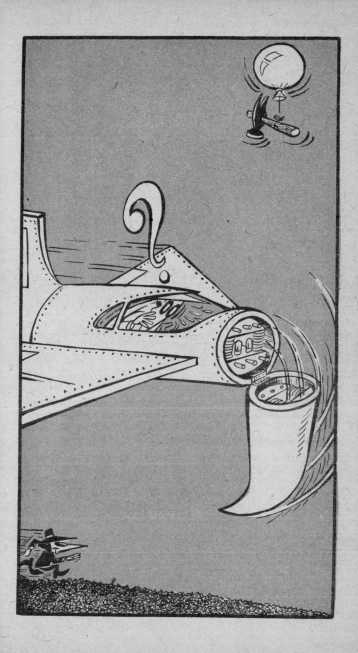

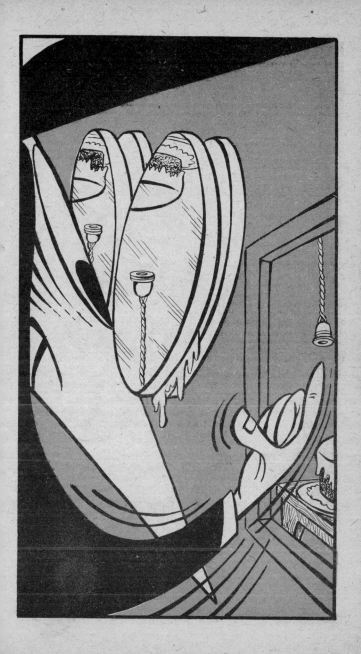

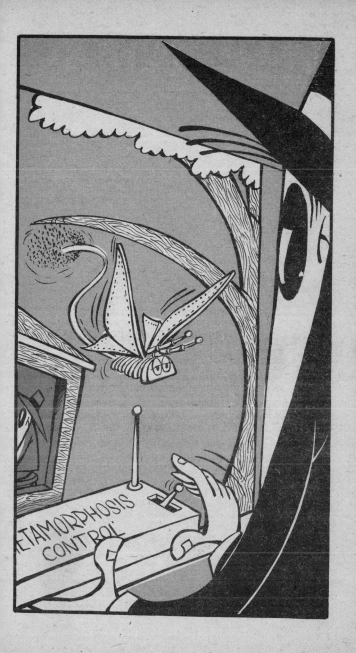

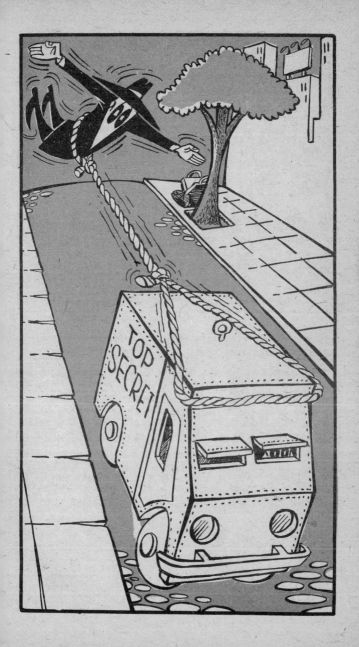

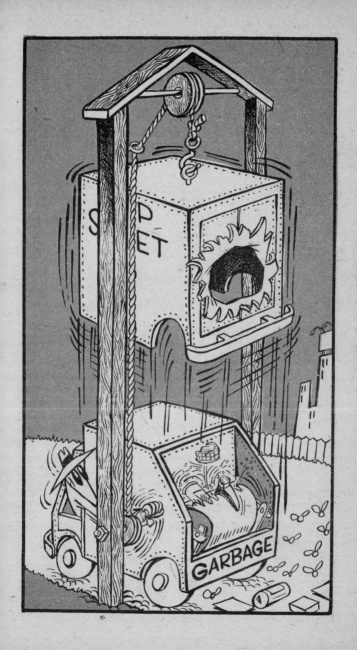

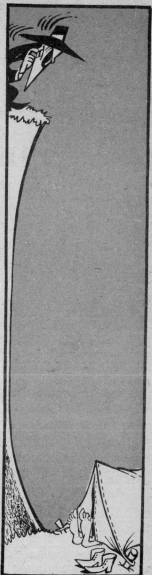

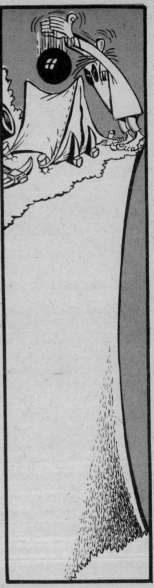

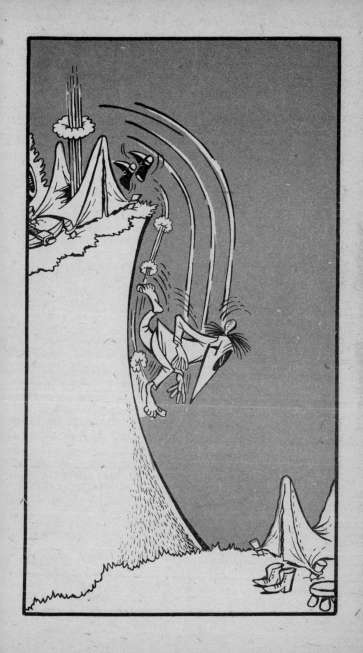

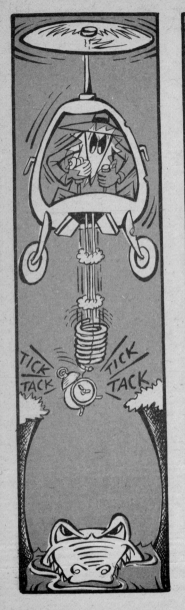

TICK TACK TICK TACK

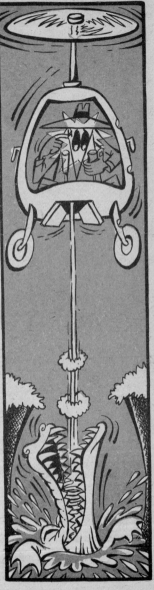

DING

Later

Still Later

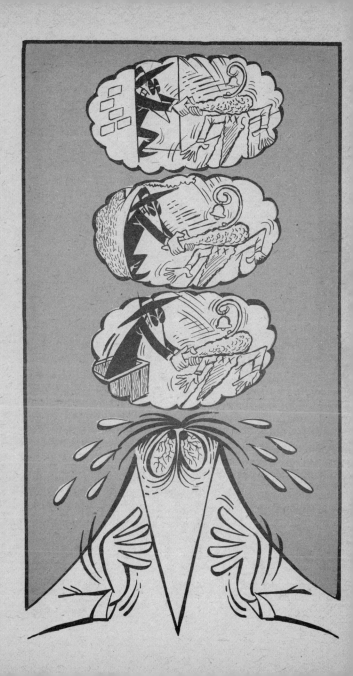

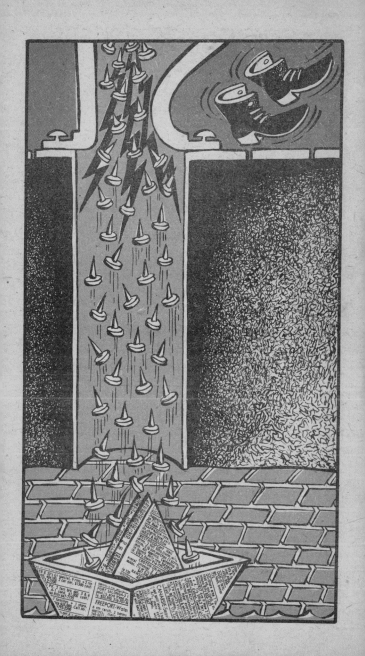